Jusst Dale

By Debby Coughlan

COPYRIGHT

For Mom, Dad, James, and Uncle Preston -

I can still hear Uncle Preston singing
"Touch me, Lord, I need thy hand of mercy."

And for Ken, Troy, KJ, Dale, and Brooks -

Thank you for jusst loving me.
You are my pride and joy.

- Dale Dunning

For Dean, Matt, and Kristin -

> Your impact on my journey is extraordinary.
> Bridges, curves, hills, and valleys—
> they're all more fun because of you.

And for Gram Dively -

> Thanks for being the very first
> *humble servant* to bless my life.
>
> *- Debby Coughlan*

CONTENTS

Special Thanks   vi

Foreword   vii

Acknowledgements   ix

Prologue   11

1	Time Travel	13
2	Finding Soup	25
3	Seeing the Light	28
4	Nothing Leftover But Love	40
5	Answering the Call	50
6	Finding Sheep	54
7	Feeding Sheep	57
8	Pastures and Soup Kitchens	62
9	Getting Ready	70
10	Faithwalking	73
11	Linked by Love	75
12	Stormy Days	80
13	Drinking It All In	89
14	Revving the Engine	104
15	The Awakening	112

Epilogue   119

About Michael Symon   121

About the Author   123

SPECIAL THANKS TO MICHAEL SYMON
Chef/Owner of Lola, Lolita, Roast and B Spot

Dale Dunning met Chef Michael Symon when they cooked together during her experience with *Extreme Makeover: Home Edition*. We are especially grateful to him for writing the heartfelt words that appear in the foreword of this book.

FOREWORD

I have been quite lucky in life to meet many amazing people, some famous, some not—and occasionally some so spectacular that I am truly taken aback by how they live their lives in a way that makes everyone around them more complete and full of joy. Dale Dunning is one of these people.

I met Dale while helping out on *Extreme Makeover*. The minute I made eye contact with her, I could feel the warmth and kindness spilling out of her body. There were no airs, no "look at all I have done," no judging, just a pure and complete selflessness that yearned to help others. In this day and age, although you hear about acts of kindness, it is few and far between that you get the chance to meet someone like Dale who will help those in need with absolutely no thought of how it is going to benefit her.

I know we often have heard people say *food heals* and I, too, believe that there is something magical about feeding those less fortunate and nurturing them back to a better place; but that day I spent with Dale was about so much more than soup. It was about the magic she created through passion and the lessons I learned about life. We could have made hot tea with lemon that day, and sharing that time with Dale would have made it one of the best meals I have ever had.

Yes, soup can heal—and soup truly does nourish—but nothing I have ever eaten made me feel so full and inspired as my day with Dale Dunning.

All my love, Dale, you are as special as they come,

- *Michael*

ACKNOWLEDGEMENTS

This book would not have been possible without the following people who have truly blessed me:

Lois Carter

Thank you for always believing in me.
You've been by my side every step of the way,
since the first pot and hot plate.

My Silent Partners

Thank you for being with me from the beginning, and for continuing to support my ministry to this day.
You have richly blessed me.

Tony Forrest

Thank you for your friendship, and for editing this book.
Your bubbly spirit has always touched my heart.

Ivana Biela

Thank you for creating the elegant cover design.
You have an extraordinary talent for bringing art to life.

Debby Coughlan

Thank you for capturing my journey in words.
Our conversations at the kitchen table created
more than a book. It inspired a friendship.

I love you all,

- *Dale*

MESSAGE FOR READERS

This book is a story based on the life and memories of Dale Dunning. Names and circumstances have been changed to respect the privacy of others. Resist the urge to read between the lines. Instead, be inspired by the message.

PROLOGUE

I've been on a long journey that started when I was a little girl. Along the way, the things I saw and the places I went made me realize that God was always with me.

The scripture says, "feed my sheep . . . care for my sheep . . . tend to my sheep." I have taken this to heart, feeding people, clothing people, giving money, hosting baby showers for mothers in need, and telling people that everything is going to be all right.

Looking back at my journey, I now realize that these are the things I wish someone had done for me when I so needed it. But I am home now and I thank God for blessing me through you.

Some people call me Pastor, some call me Reverend Dale, and others call me Mom.

But I say, thank God I am Jusst Dale.

1

Time Travel

The *Extreme Makeover* bus was rolling down the road with the three of us tucked safely inside. During the show's weeklong building projects, it was typical for families to be whisked away to Disney World while their homes underwent incredible transformations.

Since my husband's fear of flying made the long trek nearly impossible in such a short time, Ken, Brooks, and I were instead treated to a private driving tour of sights stretching from Baltimore to New York and back again. Along the way, we had a home-cooked meal in Pennsylvania, heard cheers coming from the stadium in Williamsport during the Little League World Series, and found ourselves in the middle of a power outage amid stormy weather in Maryland.

Simple experiences were magnified by our extraordinary circumstances. In a Baltimore ice cream parlor, a special flavor was created just for us. Ken, Brooks, and I mixed up custard creations and everyone voted for the best one. Brooks took the prize, despite the fact that Ken tried to sway the judging by offering the crew a week off if they chose his version. As if he had the power to do that.

The winning ice cream was named *Jusst Chicken Sooup*. It started out as plain vanilla with colorful sprinkles mixed in to represent vegetables. A few chunks of chicken-colored cookie dough were added before finishing the whole thing off with ribbons of caramel that looked like noodles. Ken liked the idea of ice cream soup best of all. Despite the fact that he had helped me open seventeen soup kitchens, Ken hadn't eaten a real bowl of soup since the day his first grade teacher tried to force some down his throat when he wasn't feeling well.

The highlight of our trip was Niagara Falls, where Brooks and I enjoyed the ride of our lives on the Maid of the Mist while Ken, in his words, "screamed like a girl." The TV crew and bus driver had become like family to us, and they delighted in our reaction to each experience.

The crew politely referred to us as *The Dunning Family,* and their famous bus had become our home away from home. Whenever I heard that reference, I had to smile, realizing how few people back home in southern Delaware knew that my full name was Dale Dunning. My brothers and sisters had given me that name—actually, Dale Bathsheba Dean—on May 22, 1953. It was the combination of my father's name, Dallas, and a character named Bathsheba they had seen in a movie. The Dunning part came later.

You see, most people back home call me Miss Dale, Pastor Dale, or simply the Soup Lady, because that's what I do. I make soup.

On a typical day, Ken and I would awaken at 2:30 a.m. to stir up recipes in our tiny kitchen and transport a random collection of pots and pans to local churches and fellowship halls. Along with our adult son, Brooks, we had been doing this for years. It was as constant as the waves that lapped the Atlantic shore just a few miles from our home. Day after day, I would grab my red hat, outline my smile with matching lipstick, and dish out ladles and ladles of soup.

I couldn't imagine doing anything else.

Debby Coughlan

Now we were on the bus, slowly making our way back to Delaware and the life we had left behind. Feeling incredibly blessed, we had no idea what to expect when we arrived at the brand new place we would soon call home.

Small towns and cornfields were flying by, and I had nothing but time on my hands. Time to think, time to reflect, and even time to let tears flow over so many memories now far behind me. Miles and miles the bus traveled as my mind journeyed through time.

I glanced over at my son, Brooks, stretched out on the recliner listening to music, as if for once he didn't have a care in the world. At the front of the bus, the driver was a captive audience being treated to endless jokes from my husband, Ken.

"How about a three piece chicken dinner?" I heard Ken ask.

I cringed, knowing Ken would then pull three kernels of corn out of his pocket and say a few words in an attempt to get a chuckle from the driver. I wondered how many times I had strained my back to pluck stray kernels from our washing machine before I started making Ken empty his pockets every night. To some people, those pockets might have seemed like junk drawers, gathering a collection of cast-off bits and pieces that would never again see the light of day. But Ken's pockets were the exact opposite of that. He had carefully selected each tiny gem—cards, kernels, photos—for a specific purpose. And he used them often.

"Ken," I called out, "I'm going to put my head down for a little nap."

Mid-joke, he smiled and waved back at me before delivering the expected chicken-dinner punch line. No doubt, the driver could probably recite it on his own by now, but he laughed just the same.

I packed up the thoughts that were bouncing around in my head, rested them on a soft pillow, and fell asleep in the back of the bus. While I dozed, memories took flight, and soon I was traveling through time.

There I was, in my early forties, sitting on the floor of our little screen porch on Wil King Road in rural Delaware, about fourteen years earlier. The porch was a special little piece of paradise Ken had built at the back of our house.

Although I had begged and pleaded for a porch, it didn't happen until Ken came home one day to find a yard full of cement blocks. I bought those chunks of concrete by saving every bit of the daily lunch money Ken had given me. Week after week, I skipped lunch and dropped the cash into a Maxwell House coffee can until I finally had enough to buy the blocks.

Ken had always wanted to be a carpenter and back then, as a builder's helper, he had just enough know-how to be dangerous with some tools and wood. Most of all, he was eager to build me the porch of my dreams. Honestly, with a pile of cement blocks in his yard, he didn't have a choice.

There was nothing fancy about the porch; in fact, part of it remained unfinished. It had taken me a lot longer to save up for it than it took Ken to build it. When it rained, sometimes the water would slide right down the exposed walls, and we'd have to stop whatever we were doing to run for buckets and bowls.

Yet, this sanctuary was where I could sink into a cozy chair and read, or nap on the sofa when I found a rare moment to rest. The kerosene heater provided warmth in the winter, and window screens welcomed the summer breeze with open arms.

There was a piano in the corner next to painted windowsills that were lined with colorful liquor bottles and random jars. Everyone contributed to my glass collection, and as a result, the display included a wide assortment of shapes and hues. Rhododendrons, peace lilies, and rubber plants occupied every square inch of space between the windows, blurring the lines between indoors and out.

This rare blend of acoustic music, makeshift stained glass, and potted plants transformed the porch into a rustic kind of holy place. It was Monday morning in September, and time for the Sweet Hour of Prayer.

Today, the first words came from Lois, a retired nurse who had seen her share of pain and suffering. At just five feet tall and under 100 pounds, she was a precious package of prayer.

"Lord, you have commanded us in your holy word to pray for the peace of Jerusalem. You've put this burden upon my heart, Father . . . I lift my people to you, Jesus, that you would bless them . . . bless them Father, bless them," Lois murmured, as a soft breeze carried her words through the window screen and on their way to the Good Lord himself.

"Amen," the room responded, "Amen, Amen."

Betsy Grace closed her eyes and began speaking while the amens were still floating in mid-air.

"Bless the soldier boys and girls, Jesus, bless 'em all. They need you more than ever Jesus, bless 'em Jesus."

"Amen," I called out from my perch on the floor, rocking my whole body from side to side. "Amen."

Betsy Grace was from Mississippi, and her sweet potato pies were a blessing all on their own. When she talked, with her southern drawl and simple words, people barely gave her the time of day. But, Lord, when that girl started to pray, the whole world stopped to listen! She was anointed to pray; there's no doubt about it.

As Betsy Grace prayed, my mind wandered back to the day after the 9/11 attack in 2001:

> *Still in shock, we didn't know what to do with ourselves, so Betsy Grace and I had marched right into the closest church we could find. When we showed up in an all-white sanctuary that day, people looked away, not quite knowing what to make of the two black women who had landed in their midst.*

Betsy Grace grabbed my arm saying, "C'mon Dale, let's get outta here, we're not welcome."

As she hustled me outside, we nearly ran over the parking attendant who caught us, mid-flight.

"Where you ladies goin'?" he called out, "The service is startin' up right now."

We didn't say a word but he knew what we were thinking.

"Now don't you girls leave; you go right on back inside," he encouraged, leaving us with nowhere else to turn.

Back inside, we were immediately absorbed into the somber crowd. The pastor asked people to pray, and that was all Betsy Grace needed to slip into her comfort zone. Right then and there, she let the words fly. As she belted out her petitions, people in that church just couldn't look away. They sat straight up like porch posts, and called out prayers of their own until the Lord shook the entire foundation of that old place.

It's a feeling I'll never forget.

By the time we left, those people treated us like we were Mother Teresa and the mother of Jesus herself. At least that's how Ken summed it up when he heard about it.

Back on Wil King Road, my little porch was still swaying with the Sweet Hour of Prayer. Thelma—or *Mama Thay* as we called her—was chanting some words of her own.

"Lord Jesus, I come with a burden for the unsaved. Heavenly Father, remember my family . . . please remember those outta the ark of safety and—"

"Amen, Amen."

"—'specially my family, Lord, I lift 'em to you in Jesus' name, please Father."

The room was humming now.

"Oh yes, yes, Amen. Yes, Lord, Amen."

Mama Thay would sometimes bring her little five-pound Pomeranian, Molly, with her. Molly had a great big bark for such a tiny pup but she was gentle as could be. I don't know, maybe that bark was Molly's way of joining in our prayers. Based on the volume, I'm sure it was a prayer filled with conviction.

I don't remember how long we'd been doing this, but once the Sweet Hour of Prayer started, it was only a matter of time before our little porch had overflowed with hand-waving, eye-clenching, God-fearing women every Monday morning. They came in all shapes and sizes, carrying every prayer you could think of—and some that you might not imagine in a million years. There must have been ten to twelve ladies who filed in week after week to share that precious hour with me.

It's funny how I always gravitated to my little spot on the floor, but during the Sweet Hour of Prayer, I wouldn't have traded that hard surface for the softest sofa. It was the perfect place to witness the glow of grateful faces beaming with thanksgiving, or to feel the hurt digging into wrinkled brows that told a painful story. When I sat in that peaceful spot and closed my eyes, the prayers surrounded me like a warm coat on a cold winter day.

In the first speck of silence, I chimed in.

"Jesus, take care of the babies in the wombs, don't let any harm or danger come to those babies, Jesus, they need you, oh Lord, bind them close."

"Amen, Amen."

"I pray for all people, young and old, men and women, gays and lesbians, blacks and whites, rich and poor, please help them know the very source of their light is You, Jesus, you love us all the same, all the same."

"Amen, yes."

Near and dear to my heart, this prayer often flowed from my lips. It was the burden of my heart to include people from every walk of life. Ever since I was a young girl, I had come across all sorts of people—and been through all kinds of things. I knew how much love was needed to overpower the fear of being different.

The little porch was talking and spinning and shaking with prayers and amens.

It wasn't always this way. Oh my, no. I didn't really come to know Jesus until it was time for my fourth son to be born.

That was after lots of twists and turns.

But I'll get into that later.

2

Finding Soup

As the bus rolled on, I fell deeper into my dream. The Sweet Hour of Prayer was drawing to a close.

"Time to go. See ya' Sunday," Mama Thay called out to me, as she shuffled the prayer group out the door, toward her conversion van parked under the big shade tree behind our house.

Several of the ladies had ridden with her, mainly because she insisted on driving and wouldn't take no for an answer. Matter of fact, Mama Thay was like a queen on a throne in the driver's seat; she wouldn't even let her husband drive that big old thing.

"See you later," I yelled out the door.

This particular day, I hardly noticed that the prayers had stopped because something curious had captured my thoughts. Amid the noise of car engines starting and tires crushing stones in our driveway, I heard it.

"Soup."

I gazed out the window, beyond the colorful glass bottles to see a striking blue sky, custom-made for September. Silence filed the air. The cars were long gone, and the sounds outside had vanished. I waited a moment, closed my eyes, and heard it again.

"Soup."

I soon realized that it was not an actual word I was hearing but an image I could feel deep inside me, yanking at my heart. Opening my eyes, I sensed the presence of the word again.

"Soup."

Rushing to the kitchen, I flung open the refrigerator and cupboard. Despite our hard times, I had chicken and vegetables and several bags of noodles right there in front of me— everything I needed for soup.

"Soup," I said to myself, staring into the cabinet. "Why soup?"

And then it hit me. I knew immediately what to do.

With my heart pounding, I reached for the phone and dialed up Pastor Short.

3

Seeing the Light

Truth be told, Ken knew Pastor Short and his wife long before I did. But, I'm getting ahead of myself; that was after the kids were born. I need to fill you in on a few details.

Our first child came when I was just seventeen and still in high school. By the time I was 29, I had four boys on my hands who kept me busy with activities, sports, and life in general.

Before I met Ken, I attended Rehoboth High School, joining the field hockey team, playing the clarinet in band, and attending all the school sporting events. In my spare time—as if there was any of that—I volunteered as a candy striper at the local hospital. Ken says that's where I became infected with the desire to help others.

Later, when the schools consolidated, I moved on to Cape Henlopen where Ken and I were high school sweethearts, but that didn't happen overnight. In fact, it might not have happened at all if Ken hadn't lingered outside the school, day after day during his senior year, waiting for me to get off the bus.

He still remembers me as the girl in the strawberry dress.

One night, I was standing alone after a football game, waiting for one of the players to give me a ride home. Although we had only spoken a few times, Ken wasn't about to miss this opportunity. Before I knew it, he appeared out of nowhere.

"I have a car, Dale. I can take you home."

He had a smile I couldn't turn down, and it was only a matter of time before we were head-over-heels in love. Yet, Ken still preferred to sit in a chair and watch at school dances while I happily skipped and twirled with my friends.

"You go along and dance," he teased. "My song is 'Save the Last Dance for Me.'"

I'm still waiting for that last dance to come along and pry him out of his chair.

Ken likes to tell a story about how I first met his dad. One evening, Ken and I were walking outside the school when we passed a bully known for picking fights at the drop of a pin. As he stomped past, we could tell he was madder than a hornet, bellyaching about being kicked out of the dance.

"I oughta go in there an' do somethin' 'bout those bastards," we heard the tough guy huff.

Just then, one of the school janitors came around the corner.

"Boy, I'm one o' those bastards you're talkin' about." Whatcha plannin' to do?"

As we hurried along, I gazed at Ken and said, "That old man's about to get beat up."

Ken looked back at me with a grin and said, "Dale, that old man's my dad. He can take care of himself. Now, let's get outta here."

More than anything, Ken loved to eat, so, whenever he talked, it was usually about food. One moonlit evening, we were on a double date in Ken's car, sitting outside the Henlopen Hotel in Rehoboth Beach. It was a busy summer evening in our resort town, with plenty of people strolling the streets.

Our friends were cuddling in the back seat while Ken sat next to me in silence, too nervous to move. We were like two statues, carved in place. I passed the time by gazing out my window, watching couples walking home from dinner, arm in arm.

Suddenly, Ken looked lovingly into my eyes and I eagerly gazed back. I slid toward him, anticipating his words—or maybe even a kiss.

"What'd you have for breakfast, Dale?"

Ken's question brought the activity in the back of the car to a stop. We were four people suspended in silence.

Soon, my friend let go of a single snicker that turned into a carload of giggles. The passing street-strollers would have never guessed that our swaying, fog-windowed vehicle was actually the result of four people howling in laughter.

Over time, our relationship developed, and Ken and I became inseparable high school sweethearts. He convinced me that we were just like the fairytale of the princess and the frog.

"Ribbit!" Ken would say, in his best frog voice, as he told people about how he had won over the girl in the strawberry dress.

He captured my heart and became my prince.

We rarely argued, but when we did, Ken would buy me a forty-five record—something like "Ain't No Mountain High Enough"—and let Diana Ross do the apologizing for him.

On October 22, 1970, our first son was born at Beebe Hospital, nine months before Ken and I were married. When I went to the hospital that day, Ken couldn't leave work to come with me. At seventeen, I remember being in so much pain and feeling just plain scared.

I lay alone in a bleached white hospital bed, thinking about so many things. I was too young to sort out the mundane and important topics swirling through my head: family, friends, homework, motherhood, football games, finances. I was excited and embarrassed all at the same time, wondering if I could handle it.

With each hour that passed, I was convincing myself that I couldn't.

In the midst of my uncertainty, the one bright spot was my nurse's aide, Marie-Sandy Dee. Just the sound of her name made me smile. Small, black and kind, she never left my side; her compassion was incredibly calming. With her reassurance, I drummed up the courage to give birth and jump headlong into the adventure of motherhood.

That day, I was unprepared for the decisions I'd need to make, beginning with my little boy's name. When Marie-Sandy Dee suggested that I call him Troy, I promised I would do that if she would stay with me. And stay she did. Even today, her image is a constant reminder to listen when someone is struggling, to be there when needed.

I kept my promise that day, too. Troy Marvel Dean earned his name from two special people in my life—a steadfast nurse's aide, and Dallas Marvel Dean, the daddy I always looked up to.

When Ken finally arrived at the hospital, he could barely hide his excitement, overwhelmed at the opportunity to see his little boy firsthand. Years earlier, when his younger sister was born, he had strained his neck to see her through a window in the basement of the hospital. Back then, that was the only place blacks were allowed.

By the time I graduated from Cape Henlopen High School in 1972, I was a wife and mother. Ken and I had married on July 9, 1971 in a small private ceremony, although he promised to give me a proper wedding on our 20th anniversary. With a little toddler on my hands, I was too busy to worry about that.

A year later, Troy had a brother named Kenneth Harmon Dunning, Jr.; we called him KJ for short. Little did I know that I was halfway on my way to four boys. Truth be told, we were just happy to have beautiful, healthy children to call our own.

Family meant the world to us; we found any way we could to be together. Ken built a little swing set in our yard and we spent nearly every night playing out there with the boys. On holidays, we'd invite family and friends to join us for cookouts, and soon our yard would be crawling with fifty people who showed up to get in on the fun. On Memorial Day, sometimes that number would swell to two hundred or more.

During that time, I attended the Wayne School and received a dental certificate, hoping to bring in some extra cash to pay the bills for our growing family. As it turned out, I never used my certificate. With the birth of our third son, Dale Dean Dunning on January 9, 1978, motherhood became more than a fulltime job. I managed to bring in a few dollars by helping the neighbors' kids get on and off the school bus each day.

It might seem like I was in over my head, but having a family was what I always wanted. In fact, when I was a little girl, I made up my mind that I would become a nurse, get married, and have seven sons. Maybe my childhood dream wasn't so far off. After all, I had studied to be a dental assistant, which was something like a nurse. And, in terms of my family plan, I was almost halfway there. My days were filled with being a homeroom mom and taking boys to Scouts, practices, and ball games.

Times weren't easy but we found ways to get by. Sometimes it was cheaper to eat out on weekends when we had coupons for pizza at Ginos or burgers at McDonalds. Ken liked to joke that if we had named one of the boys *Gino McDonald* we might have been able to eat for free now and then.

One day, in the dead of winter, the McDonalds in Rehoboth ran a Valentine special with cheeseburgers for just 20 cents each. Our car had broken down days earlier, but Ken was determined to get in on the deal. He walked six miles in a blizzard before proudly handing us a greasy bag of burgers—about twenty in all—for a grand total of $4.00. Matter of fact, he almost gave up on the way back, until he thawed out in a warm car, thanks to a Good Samaritan who happened to

be driving by when Ken was almost home—and
nearly frozen.

Ken watched *The Waltons* every week and wanted
our family to be just like that. He would say, "For
now, you stay home with the kids, Dale, but when
they get older, then follow your dream. And I'm
gonna follow right along with you."

I wasn't sure what that meant, but I always
remembered it.

One day, I went to the doctor for a routine check-
up. The nurses ran the standard tests and told me
to come back the following week.

Feeling rather sick, I had decided not to keep my
follow-up appointment. Ken insisted on taking me
there himself, so we walked in to the office
together.

"Mrs. Dunning, you're pregnant," the doctor
announced, as soon as Ken and I had settled into
the room.

"Pregnant!" I cried with tears too big to fit my eyes.
"Really?"

Ken said my knees buckled like a person who had
just been struck on the head by the Holy Spirit. I

passed out right then and there, with Ken on one side of me and the nurse on the other.

When I woke up, all I could think about was the responsibility. We barely had the money to raise three kids, let alone four. Times had been rough, and nobody had to tell me they were about to get a whole lot rougher.

Ken had to carry me to the car.

Still in shock, I actually found myself in church the following Sunday. I don't remember how I got there; we tended to be the Christmas-Easter type of worshippers. You know how that goes. In fact, this was one of the few times I had been in a sanctuary since Ken and I were married.

I remember that day like it was yesterday. The 88-year-old pastor spoke so slowly that each word became a message all its own. It seemed like he and I were the only two people in the room.

Gazing around at stained glass windows of colorful apostles and dark wooden trim etched with sacred symbols, I felt the echoes spinning around me. Words bounced off the walls and hung in the air before melting in silence. Sounds became objects that I could see, hear, and feel.

"Are you going through struggles, trials—or maybe you're just plain worn out? Do you feel like you just can't handle it all? What are you going to do about it?" The pastor's voice boomed, stirring something deep inside me.

I arched my back and shifted in the pew, growing increasingly uncomfortable. "Worn out . . . just can't handle it all," I heard, over and over.

Then, very softly, he unleashed simple words and the silence gently delivered them straight to me.

"You need Christ in your life. He loves you."

That was all it took. Before I knew it, I was at the front of the church with my knees buckling just like they did in the doctor's office. At that moment, I suddenly handed my life over to a God I didn't yet know very well.

When I walked out of church that morning, I passed by Mrs. Viola Drummond, a precious soul who often drove our boys to Sunday School. Still a bit overwhelmed at my unexpected experience, I was in need of reassurance.

I'll never forget her words.

"Dale, this is the best thing you've ever done. It's going to affect you for the rest of your life," she whispered in my ear as she gave me a hug.

And she was right.

4

Nothing Leftover But Love

Now that I was pregnant again, Ken and I attended Lamaze classes in preparation for childbirth. After three kids, you might think we didn't need the classes, but there was always more to learn and I loved the fellowship with others.

Ken, on the other hand, viewed the classes as another opportunity to eat, eagerly anticipating the snacks that were served during breaks. On the last week of class, we watched a movie about the not-so-pretty side of childbirth that turned our stomachs upside down so nobody felt like eating. Nobody except Ken, that is. As the rest of us filed out of the room, he was happy to have the snacks all to himself.

Ken likes to tell a funny story about how we ended up with four boys. I can't say it's entirely true, but I think he believes it. It's a long tale about having the proper chicken-to-child ratio to make sure we wouldn't have leftovers after dinner. I'll give you the short version but you can ask Ken to share the whole story if you run into him sometime.

They don't call Delaware the *Blue Hen State* for nothing, so you can guess what we usually had for dinner. Back then, we could buy a whole chicken for just under $2.00, and with our small family, we always had leftovers. In Ken's mind, it stood to reason that, if we couldn't finish an entire chicken in one sitting, it meant we needed another mouth to feed.

After KJ came along, we had the perfect situation: one chicken was ideal for our family of four. That is, until one night when Ken forgot to eat dinner after excitedly celebrating a pay raise. He was so happy I think he even danced a little that night. The next day, Ken looked at the leftover chicken and decided we needed to make another baby that very night.

Once Dale was born, of course one chicken wasn't enough. We plunked down $4.00 and bought two. With two chickens, we were faced with leftovers again until Brooks was born. So, despite—or maybe because of—the chicken situation, on March 31, 1982, Ken and I happily welcomed Brooks Curtis Dunning into the world with open arms.

When people ask why I use chicken in just about everything I make, Ken matter-of-factly explains that I'm avoiding leftovers. Most people don't understand what that really means, but who knows, maybe it's true. We might have had a lot more kids by now, just to get that chicken-to-child situation right.

Of course this was all in good fun. We loved every inch of our boys. No matter what happened, I knew faith would get us through, but I didn't have a minute in my day or a dime in my pocket to spare.

And neither did Ken. He was working three jobs just to put food on our table and even that was a struggle. During the day, he read meters for the local power company, putting plenty of wear and tear on his rusty car and stocky legs.

Most evenings, he'd rush home, shove the greasy old lawnmower into the trunk of our olive green '66 Chevy and cut as many lawns as he could before sunset. On weekends, he was often lucky enough to get a limo-driving job or two, and those tips sometimes made all the difference in how we dressed and ate for the time being.

Most people don't know it, but I drove the limousine long before Ken did. After Brooks was born, it became harder and harder to make ends meet. In fact, there were plenty of times when you might say the ends in our household were dangling like useless tassels on a worn out sofa cushion.

But we didn't let finances come between us. Ken always said if we could get past the money issues, we could get through anything. He was right; we had each other. Whenever we ran into financial trouble, we held on for dear life and jumped in together.

One day, when I was on my way to the Food Lion where I always shopped for groceries, I noticed a limousine parked in front of a house with a long driveway. I pulled in, marched right up to the door of that house, and rapped my knuckles against the trim.

The door opened and I was eye-to-eye with a man who didn't say a word. Or maybe he didn't have a chance to talk because I blurted out my thoughts at the first sight of him.

"I want to be your limo driver," I said, with my best Dale Dunning smile, like I was applying for a job he had advertised.

"You mean you wanna ride—" he started to say.

"No," I interrupted, "I want to be a driver."

"Now, darlin', where do you want me to take you and your girls?" he asked, looking at me sideways.

"Nowhere," I said again, "I want to be your driver."

This went on for quite some time before the man realized I was as serious as a woman with four young mouths to feed. After a long silence, he looked at me in a way that said he might be figuring out how to get me off his front porch.

"I'll call you," he said.

I had barely given him my number when the door clicked shut. Turning on one foot, I went right on to the Food Lion to do my shopping.

You can imagine my surprise when I answered the phone the following week and heard a man's voice say, "Girl, I'm gonna teach you how to drive a limo. You can practice by taking me and my boys down to the Rudder."

I didn't miss a beat, asking, "Can I bring my husband along?"

"Sure thing."

And that's how it all started. He showed me the right way to pull up, swing around a corner, and go wherever I needed to in that fancy car. I learned quickly and loved driving. But he didn't have to tell me a thing about how to treat the customers.

Taking care of people was already in my blood.

After hanging up the phone from his call, I started creating my outfit, gathering a white tuxedo, a top hat, and white gloves, too. When I finally had my turn in the driver's seat, I made the passengers feel like they were the only creatures on earth. They smiled at me—all done up in white—and told me I looked just like Michael Jackson.

One New Year's Eve, I delivered a group of partiers to the Starboard in Dewey Beach, a favorite hangout for the younger crowd. Huddled in the car, Ken and I heard their hoots and hollers at midnight, as we rang in the new year with sparkling cider. An hour or so later, I stepped outside the limo in my white getup to look for customers who might be ready to head home.

Just then, a thin woman stumbled up to me.

"Are you real or . . . maybe, maybe an angel or . . ."
Her words ran together, almost indistinguishable.

At that moment, she fell headfirst into the street
and cut her face.

Seeing the blood dripping from her cheek, her
friends screamed for an ambulance. I kneeled next
to her, dabbing at her face with my scarf.

I thought about the words I had heard in church
and quietly prayed with her, "Jesus loves you, girl,
you'll be alright."

And the bleeding stopped.

She got halfway up and looked at me again. "Are
you real?" she asked again. "Or maybe an angel?"

"I'm just a limo driver," I laughed. "But what I said
is true. Jesus does love you."

She fell down again, said a prayer, and I believe she
was saved, right then and there—drunk and all.

With all the commotion in the street, cars had
somehow managed to move around us. It was
after 1:00 a.m. on New Year's Day, and most of the

people shouldn't have been driving at all. I knew we needed to get out of the street.

I looked around, smiled back at her and added, "Honey, if you don't get out of the road right now, you'll be meeting Jesus face to face tonight."

Two years into the driving job, it became increasingly difficult to be away from the boys so I trained Ken to take my place, and that's how he got his start. Later, Troy went off to college and the other boys were old enough to stay home on their own. When I had the chance, I would ride along with Ken as he chauffeured people around, just so we could be together.

Now there's one thing you need to know about Ken. He's a people-person. To Ken, his daily work has a lot more to do with meeting folks than with driving cars, checking meters, or mowing lawns. He makes it a point to wave or talk to just about everyone he sees along the way. People love him.

And he manages to get in a joke or two as often as possible.

"Have you seen my pride and joy?" Ken always asks his latest victim. The new acquaintance becomes bright-eyed, eagerly ready to enjoy a heartwarming family photo. And that's when Ken smiles the biggest, as his new friend rolls in laughter, bewildered at the sight of a beautifully framed picture of Pride laundry detergent and Joy dish soap. Whenever I think he's handed out the last one of those wrinkled photos, he pulls another one out of his wallet. I'm not even sure where he gets them. If we had a dime for every time he shared one of those pictures, we might have avoided a lot of financial trouble down the road. But you'll hear about that soon enough.

The bottom line is, Ken truly cares about the people he serves. Matter of fact, somewhere along the line, during his 48 years of cutting lawns, Ken came up with his own policy about what to do when his customers or their family members passed away. In those cases, he cut their grass free of charge—for the rest of the year. That's just his way. Despite what this means for our home finances, I couldn't be prouder of him. He loves his customers and treats them like family.

Ken and the boys mowed yards all over the county, but Ken always said one yard was the luckiest. I never thought about a yard being lucky, but after I heard his story, I understood.

One day, he and the boys were cutting a lawn on a side street in Lewes. It was just a few blocks from the beach, where you could taste the salt in the air.

The owners were gone for the season, and Ken kept the yard in shape while they were away.

All of a sudden, Troy ran up to Ken saying, "Dad, is this real, is it, is it?"

Ken looked down and saw a handful of $20 bills in Troy's hand—maybe $200 in all.

"Boy, where'd you find that; now tell me, where'd that come from?

Ken looked around. It was long past the busy season; the street was deserted.

"Dad, it was right here in the yard, right here, just scattered all around."

"Gee whiz, what a lucky yard!"

If we're not careful, we can miss the blessings that are right in front of us.

5

Answering the Call

And that brings me back to Pastor Short.

Ken especially enjoyed visiting with Pastor Short and his wife when his meter-reading job took him to the neighborhood where their home and little church were located. He first met the Shorts when he noticed puppies playing in their yard—nine or ten of them in all. After a couple of conversations that took place over squirming puppies that required lots of belly-scratching, Ken and Pastor Short became good friends.

One day, Ken noticed Pastor Short pounding a sign into the front yard of the church.

"Whatcha doin' with that old sign, Pastor? Is the church up for sale?" Ken teased.

"Oh my no," laughed Pastor Short. I'm starting a Bible College right here on this very spot. Studying for a Master's Degree, and this is all part of it."

And he was right. The sign read, 'Sussex County School of Theology.'

As it turned out, that little sign changed my life.

Ken came home and told me about the Bible College and I called Pastor Short that very night. By the next day, I was the first student enrolled at Sussex County School of Theology—right there in Georgetown, Delaware.

I loved the classes and the people I met at Bible College. They were like family to me. We called each other *sisters and brothers in Christ*, and I was proud to be *Sister Dale*. Pastor Short's wife always brought us drinks and snacks to enjoy while we shared stories during breaks. There was something very satisfying about feeding our stomachs and souls at the same time. It made perfect sense.

By then, I was coming face to face with the God I had encountered years earlier when I suddenly knelt in church. Now, I was studying to be a pastor. Although it felt good, I had no idea where it was leading me.

Back on Wil King Road, the image of soup came to me that Monday in September when I was drawn to my kitchen after the Sweet Hour of Prayer. Replaying this in my dream, I saw the light and heard a call that was aimed straight at me.

John 21: 15-17 stood out like a beautiful painting in my mind. Jesus was speaking to Peter, but it was like I was right there with them.

"If you love me, feed my lambs. If you love me, take care of my sheep."

Suddenly, my mind was made up, clear as could be. I wasn't going to wait for people to come to me. I would go to them. I wouldn't serve *in* a church. Oh no, I would *be* the church right here in my little world.

Apparently, the vehicle that would get me there was soup.

Dialing my phone from the kitchen that day, I couldn't wait to hear a voice on the other end of the line. "Pastor Short," I said calmly. "Would it be alright if I bring soup to share after class tomorrow?"

"Sure baby," he responded before I could go on. That's how he always talked to us, just like we were one of his own.

And I started making soup right then and there. The very first place I would *be* the church was in the comfort of the Bible College with my brothers and sisters in Christ.

But it wouldn't be the last.

Chicken Noodle Soup, by Dale Dunning

Ingredients:
1 whole chicken, cut up
4 diced onions
1 bag frozen vegetables
2 bags extra wide noodles
2 cups water
2 cups chicken broth
Prayer
Love

In a large pot, add chicken, water and chicken broth. Cook 45 minutes to an hour on medium high until done. Remove chicken and let it cool. Pull chicken from bone. Bring broth to boil and add noodles, vegetables, and chicken pieces. Add salt and pepper to taste. Check for tenderness of noodles. Pray that it will be the best-tasting soup in town. Serve it with love in your heart.

6

Finding Sheep

"Sister Dale brought soup for us," Pastor Short exclaimed when we took our break the next day.

Except for the little hot plate supplied by Mrs. Short, I brought everything I needed for my labor of love. And it continued all four years while I attended Bible College.

To me, it wasn't a labor at all. Making soup was like brushing my teeth or wearing my favorite hat. It's just what I did.

When the ladies at the Sweet Hour of Prayer told me about friends who were sick, lonely, or depressed, I decided it was time for my little soup ministry to grow. So, I started making more soup—not just for my family at the Bible College— but for precious brothers and sisters I hadn't even met.

"Gracious this is good," an ailing aunt of a friend would say when I delivered my soup. My heart became as warm as the broth in my hands.

When I sat on the floor during the Sweet Hour of Prayer, I started listening more intently about the people who were being prayed *for.* That's where my soup and I would go—wherever people were in need.

We would simply follow the prayers. Together, my soup and I would *be* the church out in the world.

After that, when I made soup, something found its way to my heart, kindling a flame that had flickered in and out through the years. I believed in the power of prayer, but making soup taught me to listen in ways I never had before.

I became a soup scientist, experimenting with endless flavors and techniques. Along the way, I discovered that chicken noodle soup is somewhat overrated when it comes to healing powers. In hard times, any sort of soup will do: chicken noodle, beef and vegetable, split pea, whatever. Each one becomes a miracle-working ingredient.

Because, in the end, it isn't really about soup at all. It is about the meaning floating *in* the soup, drifting in the scented steam that rises above each bowl. The best way I can explain it is this: it is impossible to make soup and deliver it to someone in need without caring.

In other words, *soup equals care.*

Armed with an arsenal of crockpots and utensils, my soup ministry grew. When I took food to struggling people, they ate it up—literally and figuratively—and they told me about others who would benefit from the goodwill that was dished up along the way. For me, this newfound mission was as simple as getting up out of my chair rather than sitting still when I heard about a person in need.

All the while, Ken and I continued to struggle with our own finances and trying to make ends meet. Yet, somehow, we always found the time and money to provide for others.

It was becoming clear that my pastoring path would be far from typical. I was using a simple pot of soup to make a difference in the world—one person at a time. My ministry involved making soup with faith, serving it with love, and letting the Spirit handle the rest.

I couldn't have stopped that process if I wanted to.

7

Feeding Sheep

It was ordination day, and there I was at the New Abundant Church of God and Christ in Fort Lauderdale, Florida. After studying theology, making soup, and bonding with my brothers and sisters at the Bible College, I was finally ready to become a pastor. All those years of preparation boiled down to just a few treasured moments, when Bishop Claire laid her hands on my head and delivered me into the Lord's service.

It had special meaning for me to be ordained by Bishop Claire; she was my neighbor's sister, and that's why we had traveled all the way to Florida for the ordination. I could feel the power of God whirling all around and lifting my spirit when she prayed.

I left that place with a whole new soul.

Several years later, back in Delaware, one of our sons was working at the Cape Gazette, the local newspaper in town. One day, he and I were sitting in the kitchen, talking.

"Mom, what do you call what you're doing?" he asked.

"What do you mean, son?"

"Well, you spend all your time and money making soup and taking it around to everyone," he said, his tone straightforward.

Agreeing with him, I started to explain, "Well, yes, I do, and—"

Before I could continue, he went on, "And you graduated from the Bible College, but you're not a pastor at a church." With a sigh he added, "So, what are you *doing*?"

"Listen," I answered, "there are so many hungry people in this world—more than you realize. And making soup is one of the things I do best. When I take soup to people, it seems to make them feel better. Helping them makes *me* feel better, too. And by the way, I don't have to be standing in a church or shouting from a big old pulpit to be a pastor. I guess I just want a place where I can help people . . . in my own way."

"Well, then what do you call *that*?" he asked.

"I don't know," I answered, but, right then and there, I started to pray about it. My own son had me thinking, and maybe even questioning what I was doing.

And, sure enough, that night it came to me in a message from the Holy Spirit.

Now, people often think that a message from the Spirit has to be spooky, strange, and mysterious. Or maybe something a religious fanatic dreams up to get attention. But this wasn't that way at all.

In fact, it was almost humorous.

As I prayed about my ministry, the Spirit showed me the words as plain as day: "It's *Jusst Sooup*, Dale, *Jusst Sooup*." In my mind, the words were drawn out in a funny exaggerated way because the Spirit was making a point—as if to say, "for Pete's sake, Dale, it's no big deal. It's just soup after all, simple as that. Nothing complicated. Keep your focus on me and you can handle it."

Finally content, I smiled and drifted off to sleep. The next morning, I couldn't wait to tell my son the news. My ministry would feed people's bodies and souls and it would be called *Jusst Sooup*. I wrote it that way, adding the extra letters, because it reminded me to focus on the simplicity of the mission, without taking things too seriously. It was *Jusst Sooup*, after all—exactly as the Spirit had explained.

Now that I was ordained, I would be a pastor out in the world—not hidden inside a church. And that was *more* than just okay. I decided it was what the world *needed*.

My son mentioned our conversation to a reporter at the Cape Gazette who later took the time to interview me and write a story. After the article ran, Rev. Dr. Harry Hughes—everyone called him Pastor Buzz—gave me a call.

"Hi Dale, this is Buzz Hughes. I read about you in the Cape. We'd like you to run a soup kitchen in our church."

And that's how it all started. On April 5, 2005, my first soup kitchen was officially underway at Lewes Presbyterian Church.

I had found my calling and started serving it up—
one bowl at a time.

8

Pastures and Soup Kitchens

Over the years, many more soup kitchens would follow. But being the church in so many places required more and more resources. It had taken me nine months to save the money for my first crockpot—while also paying for gas, studies, ingredients, and supplies. Soon, my inventory grew from one, to seven, to fourteen crockpots, many of them funded through house cleanings, limo shifts, and lawn mowing jobs. Ken and I put everyone in the family to work; the boys pitched in as soon as they were old enough to pick up a rake or dishrag.

But it wasn't always easy. Soup kitchens speak such a quiet language that some folks can't hear the real message over the noise of their own fears. People see hurt faces or dirty clothes and make instant assumptions. They hear rumors and cultivate doubt. They make decisions, close windows, and lock doors.

And then I come along and open things up.

Over the course of opening kitchens, I've been called every name imaginable—even had soup tossed in my face a few times. I've been welcomed by pastors and shunned by church members—and vice versa, too. I've dealt with unexpectedly locked cabinets and deliberately disconnected electrical service. I've endured two-faced volunteers who served stingy portions to starving people so they could save my soup for profit-making plans. I've fixed broken-down boilers and plunged my way out of backed-up bathrooms. You might say I've seen it all.

But I always found a way.

During this time, I was still driving the limo now and then, or at least riding along with Ken when he took over. We were always respectful of our passengers' privacy, but now and then, it was hard to ignore a heated conversation coming from the back seat. In those cases, Ken loved to nonchalantly mention that I was a pastor, loud enough to be sure it was overhead. By the time we dropped the people off, we had shared some laughs, and they'd be giggling and holding hands. That's just how it went.

I didn't look for rewards, but I often ran into one when I least expected it. Remember the lady who fell in the street outside the Starboard on New Year's Eve? She appeared out of nowhere in one of my first soup kitchens, just to thank me.

One time, before Thanksgiving, Ken and I were having big financial problems and found ourselves three months behind on mortgage payments. There was no way around it. We were about to lose our house.

Ken gathered up his nerves and plodded along the sidewalk toward a home where he had worked for years. It was a block away from the house with the lucky yard. These were kind people who had always taken the time to visit with him, and he didn't know where else to turn.

As Ken started up the steps, he thought of running the other way, just when he saw the man's familiar face at the door. It was too late to turn back. He started talking before the man could say hello.

"Sir, I got somethin' to ask you, and I'm sorry to interrupt your evenin' now."

"It's okay, Ken, have a seat."

Ken remained standing and went on. "There's no way but to just say it. It's like this. Dale and I are havin' a rough time, I guess you could say money problems, and I'm afraid we're about to lose our house . . . and I don't really know what to do. Need some money to cover the mortgage, and like I said, I don't know where else to turn. Thought maybe you'd have an idea . . ."

Ken had managed to get some words out, and there was nothing left to do but wait for a response.

"It's okay, Ken," the man said quietly, "Let me talk to my wife." He paused and added, "Come back tomorrow; I'll let you know what we can do."

The whole conversation had been over so quickly, and it weighed heavily on Ken's mind. That night, he agonized over it, repeating each word to me, and replaying the discussion in his own head many times. He was feeling ashamed about asking for such a big favor. We never did that. When we needed something, Ken and I just took on another job to drum up the money. But it finally caught up with us. We'd been pouring most of our funds into feeding others and hadn't noticed what it was doing to our own lives. We were in over our heads, with no solution in sight. We barely had a penny to our name.

The next day, Ken thought about forgetting the whole thing. He didn't want to bother his customer again. Maybe there was some other way; perhaps he could work nights somewhere. But we both knew it would take too much time to catch up, and we were getting more behind every day. Plus, Ken had promised to go back to the house, and he was a man of his word.

Before Ken's foot hit the top step of the porch, his customer opened the door.

"Well, hi Ken, come on in," a voice said stoically, in a tone that hovered slightly beyond comfort. Ken leaned against a wall to listen. The house was pleasant but quiet.

"I have something to tell you, Ken. My wife and I had a good talk last night, and I can't stop thinking about what she said. It makes a lot of sense. When I explained your situation, the first thing she said was, 'If you loan money to friends, it always causes a problem.'"

The word *problem* seemed to linger in the room like an unwanted guest. Ken wished the TV was blaring in the background, or maybe a radio, anything to cover up the words he was afraid to hear.

The man went on. "And, you know, she's probably right about that. We consider you and Dale as our friends, don't you see? It just won't work for us to lend you the money. You know what I mean?"

Ken shifted back and forth, wanting to vanish into thin air, so he wouldn't have to gather the strength to turn and walk away.

"Sure, sure," he said, "we know."

But the man went on. "Like I said, Ken, you've helped us out for years, mowing our lawn and taking care of our place, just like it was your own. Why, you take better care of it than we ever could. You and Dale have become our friends."

Ken smiled and let the word *friends* settle into his mind. That word meant a lot, even if it did interfere with the loan we needed.

Just then, he realized the man was still talking.

"Ken, we could never loan you the money. We're going to give it to you."

Ken was so nervous he thought he was hearing things.

"Really . . . really? You sure you wanna do that?"

Right then and there, that man gave Ken the money to cover our debt—with a little left over to buy the kids some Christmas presents.

"Thank you," Ken said quietly, his eyes about to overflow. Words seemed so inadequate. "You don't know what this means to us."

Ken walked slowly down the steps, deep in thought. Stopping for a moment, he looked down the block toward the yard where Troy had found the money months earlier.

Maybe that was no coincidence either.

Through all the ups and downs, the one constant was the time we spent serving soup. Whenever I worked in a new location, I would flash back to the very first kitchen I could remember. It was where I had learned to cook, watching my mother in her perfectly-pressed apron as she moved effortlessly across our tiny kitchen. I studied every move she made, and fetched water from the outdoor well when she needed it. The whole time, she smiled and hummed, turning piles of powder and tidbits of meat into meals that were meant to merely feed but destined to truly nourish.

Through the years, Ken and I kept opening soup kitchens, almost without realizing it, until we had started seventeen in all. You may think that every soup kitchen was the same, filled with pots, pans, bowls, and hungry people.

That couldn't have been further from the truth.

Each soup kitchen stood out in its own way, as different as the untold stories behind every silent face you pass when you walk down the street.

9

Getting Ready

I awoke to realize that the *Extreme Makeover* bus had rolled to a stop. Hearing water rush over the metal roof, I wondered if the bus had pulled over amid a summer thunderstorm. My Lord, that was all we needed. Last week, a hurricane had marched across the East Coast, knocking power out of our hotel in Maryland. We still weren't sure how the bad weather might have impacted our new home.

I tried not to think about that and went up to the front of the bus to see what was going on.

"Well, hi there Miss Dale, did you have a little nap?" the bus driver asked.

"Uh huh," I responded, still half asleep. I loved our bus driver. He always took the time to chat.

"It won't be long now; we're getting the bus all spiffy so it'll be ready for the big entrance."

"What?" I asked, confused.

"It's being washed, right now," he said, with words that explained the rushing water I'd heard.

"Oh, I see. Where are we?"

"Wilmington, just a couple of hours now, Miss Dale. Ken and Brooks went to McDonalds. Are you hungry?"

"No, thanks, I'm still waking up. Think I'll just read and relax awhile."

Before I settled in with my book, I looked out the window and saw Ken walking across the parking lot with Brooks. Dear sweet Ken. He and I had been through so much, but I never had time to really dwell on that before. I watched Ken and Brooks disappear into McDonalds.

At that moment, all I could think of was how often Ken had made me smile. He kept his promise about our wedding. On our 20th anniversary, we renewed our vows in a special ceremony at the Catholic church in Lewes. There were only about five people at our original wedding, but the second time around we shared the day with more than 500 friends.

I smiled and rested my head on a pillow, laying the book in my lap as I stared at the ceiling. My thoughts shifted to all the soup kitchens Ken and I had seen over so many years.

Soup kitchens are spectacular places. They're full of hope, brimming with people teetering on the edge of possibility, hungering not so much for food as for a nudge in the right direction.

Now wide-awake but knee-deep in memories, I thought about those precious people. They are the singular souls who helped me shape *Jusst Sooup* into the gentle force that would roll up its sleeves and find people *wherever* and *however* they happened to be.

It would turn out to be a ministry like no other.

10

Faithwalking

As I glanced into space, memories carried me along a graceful current of faith. I was hand-in-hand with people I had met during my ministry—those life-changing singular souls. I looked around and saw so many of them moving by, right next to me. They were stark reminders that everyone is struggling, everyone is searching.

In my thoughts, we kept flowing together, like a mighty river. As I floated along in this stream of people, I saw one who was divorced, another who was an alcoholic, and someone else who was pregnant and lonely. And there were so many more, dealing with trials beyond imagination.

Each one of them was balancing on that fragile, precious edge, in need of healing and hope.

We had met over soup, but we never stopped walking together.

11

Linked by Love

As I meandered through my thoughts, the first to pull at my heart was Sophia, a young girl who had appeared at the soup kitchen long ago, looking lost and frightened.

Sophia's Story:

The slender girl almost went unnoticed until I caught a glimpse of her in the corner. She was in her early twenties, and I could tell she was distressed.

"You all right?" I asked, surprising her from behind.

"Not really, she muttered. "But you wouldn't understand."

Quietly, I asked for her name. Amid the noise of clattering dishes and idle conversation, she whispered, "Sophia."

And then she murmured even more softly, "I can't have this baby. Just can't do it . . . I'm not going to have the baby."

"Sophia, what a pretty name," I said, stalling for time to put my thoughts together. "I'm glad you're here. You can talk to me."

"I said you wouldn't understand," she stated, emphasizing each word, as if I hadn't heard.

Now that I had taken the time to think a bit, I ignored her tough tone and jumped right in.

"I guess you're partly right, Sophia; I don't know anything about abortion, if that's what you're talking about, because I can't say I've ever gone through that," I said, looking straight into her watery eyes. "But people have come in here talking about it, struggling with it. Some people have gotten through it; others told me it tormented them for life."

I noticed she was listening more intently so I took the opportunity to go on. "Now, on the other hand, I can tell you about a young girl like you—actually much younger than you—who got pregnant, had the baby, and later married the father of that child. Turns out, he loved her very much."

"Well," she said, "that's not true . . . life just isn't that way because—"

"Listen, Sophia." I said before she could finish her sentence. "What if I told you that you're talking to that girl right now, right here?"

She started to interrupt, but I was on a roll.

"When I graduated from high school, I already had a little boy. I was just a child raising a child. I know what you're going through because I've been there and I've struggled through it. And I'm here to tell you that, even though it's not easy, it's okay. You need to know that you're okay."

"But, I'm scared and alone and . . . and I don't have a doctor. I'm not going to one of those free clinics and get treated like a pathetic piece of welfare. I've seen those places . . . scares me to death. I can't go, just can't . . ." Her voice trailed off as she looked down, tears falling into her lap.

I put my hand on her shoulder and she looked up at me. "Everyone has a bump in the road now and then, Sophia, and this is yours right now. I got through it, other people got through it, and you will, too. It doesn't matter if you go to a free clinic or a great big old hospital. I've seen good and bad things at both. What really matters is that you take care of yourself—and that baby of yours."

Sofia looked down again when I mentioned the baby. I could barely hear her when she said, "It's so hard, Miss Dale, so hard . . ."

"Of course it's hard," I whispered. "Just look at all the people around you in this soup kitchen. Look at them. Have you ever really looked into their eyes? Why do you think these people are here? Everyone has something going on. Some people will walk out of here today and they'll keep digging themselves deeper into holes they can't possibly get out of. But I know there are a few brave ones who will do something about it."

I waited a long time, letting my words wander anonymously to each face in the room.

Then I added, "You just have to make up your mind to be one of the brave ones, Sophia. Nobody can do that part for you."

Sophia didn't say much more that day, but she kept coming back to the soup kitchen and we talked often. I told her about how much Ken and I loved and supported each other through all the ups and downs. Back in those days, whether our decisions were right or wrong, they were all part of growing up. We were just kids, finding our way in the world, and just like everyone else, sometimes Ken and I chose a winding, difficult path.

The more we shared our life stories together over countless bowls of soup, the more I saw hope return to Sophia's life.

As Sophia drifted from my thoughts, I smiled and imagined someone walking with her on the other side. It might have been a little girl.

In my mind's eye, I couldn't be sure.

12

Stormy Days

With Ken and Brooks back on the bus, we had slowly made our way to the edge of a small town. Gazing out the window, I noticed a school with a few bikes neatly stacked in a gray rack shaded by the red brick building. My thoughts turned to a bike rider I had met long ago.

Saul's Search:

It must have been 95 or 100 degrees that day and it was hard to breathe, even when you were standing still. The thick humidity hit you like a load of cement blocks as soon as you stepped one foot out of the house.

When he made it to the soup kitchen, the old man fell off his bike and lay motionless in the dusty church parking lot. A few loose stones were strewn around where the tire had skidded to a stop. The air was filled with light, powdery dust.

One of my Soupers—that's what I called some of the regulars at the soup kitchen—was the first to notice him.

"Hey, there's somebody layin' in the parkin' lot, Miss Dale," I heard through the screen door.

I dropped the towel from my hand and rushed out the door with another volunteer on my heels. We lifted the man up, brought him into the air conditioning, and gave him some cold lemonade.

He started babbling as soon as he caught his breath. "Well, I jus' hadda come here, jus' hadda come. I heard 'bout this soup an' people say it's so good, an' I haven't ate for awhile and I hadda make it here. Can I eat?"

The questions started to pour out of the Soupers who weren't one bit afraid to get right in the face of someone new. At the soup kitchen, they thought everything was everyone's business.

"Man, how long you been ridin'?" "Where you from?" and "What's your name?"

"Name's Saul. Jus' rode in from Greenwood," he mumbled. "Reckon I been ridin' a few hours. Stopped whenever I could find a little piece o' shade but there wasn't much o' that out on the main road."

All eyes in the room widened. Greenwood was more than thirty miles away—a long trip for a feeble rider with a wobbly old bike on a blazing hot day.

After he'd eaten some soup and shared stories with the regulars, I let Saul lay down for a while on one of the cots in the basement below the soup kitchen. On this morning, the beds were empty, but there were many days when they were blanketed with alcoholics sleeping off a bad night, or lonely people searching for warmth in the middle of a cold spell.

After Saul was settled in, I went back to my work upstairs.

People came and went, and before I knew it, it was after 3:00 p.m. and old Saul and I were the only ones left. I went downstairs and found him sound asleep. Finally, he had settled down and seemed to be breathing normally.

While Saul slept, I sat on the cot across from him, remembering how our family had struggled through so many misfortunes of our own—so many unexpected twists and turns. Looking deep into his red hot forehead, I flashed back to the day I had skipped home from elementary school on St. Patrick's Day to learn that my house had burned clean to the ground. Only the chimney was left standing, like a loyal soldier guarding the useless pile of ashes that represented everything we had.

The comforting memories of childhood are captured in such small moments, and some of those, too, were buried in that stack of soot. After the fire, it was the absence of those moments that I remembered most: the precious seconds lost, the way Mommy and Daddy seemed to change. I missed walking to the mailbox with Daddy after school, and searching for surprises in his lunchbox when he returned from work. Those were our routines before the fire, but I don't remember ever doing them again.

Losing everything you have is one of the most humbling experiences on the face of this earth. But there comes a day when you realize that you still have all the things that matter—family, friends, those black and white pictures tacked forever on the wall of your mind. And something makes you hang on to hope, believing you'll someday find new moments to capture and frame.

By then it was almost 4:00. I looked back at Saul, thought about heading out into the hot, sticky evening, and remembered all the intense weather we had endured through so many years of soup kitchens. In the summertime, we lugged soup around in boiling hot weather with sweat flowing like a river from every inch of our bodies. By mid-winter, we were carrying broth through blinding snowstorms, wearing the hot pans like mittens to keep our fingers warm.

On one of those cold days, I went to the soup kitchen earlier than normal. We were in the midst of a sudden, severe cold snap in January that had followed unusually warm weather. It must have been about 25 degrees, and people weren't ready for it. Matter of fact, they'd been wearing short sleeves and flip-flops the week before.

Sure enough, when I got to the soup kitchen, there were some young men lying on the bench with their eyes almost frozen shut. I don't know what would have happened to them if I hadn't stopped by early that day, but they were happy to thaw out in the soup kitchen.

And that made me happy, too.

Truth be told, our family had survived a lot of threatening weather through the years. Once, Ken was working at the power company with no way to get home after an unexpected blizzard blew in. A co-worker gave him a ride as far as he could, but the roads were bad and Ken had to walk the last two miles. He was lugging a trash bag full of groceries he had quickly bought when they left the office, and must have looked like Santa Claus with it hoisted over his shoulder. As darkness fell, he walked in snow above his knees with icy flurries blowing straight into his face. Several times along the way, he thought about leaving the heavy bag behind, but he knew we would need the food to weather the storm. So he plowed through the snow and finally made it. A cell phone would have helped, but that was long before anyone around here had one of those.

Thinking about the cell phone reminded me that it was getting late, and I still needed to find a place for Saul to spend the night. While he slept, I punched numbers into the phone until my fingers were tired. On about the ninth try, I finally found someone who would let him stay for a night or two while he got some plans together. I had no choice but to make those calls—motel prices in our resort town were sky high in the summertime.

After Saul got through a couple nights, I bought him a bus pass so he could get on his way.

I overheard Ken and Brooks talking near the front of the bus, redirecting my thoughts away from that day so long ago with Saul. They were imagining our new home, wondering how different life might be in the weeks to come.

Where had the time gone anyway—not just the week we'd been away, but all the years and trials we'd come through? Despite our hard work and help from others, Ken and I had finally lost our house to foreclosure a few years earlier. Having endured the demise of two homes in my life—one to fire and another to foreclosure—I'm not sure which is worse.

I think I'd choose the fire.

At least a fire inflicts its pain in one quick and merciful motion, like ripping a Band-Aid from tender skin. A foreclosure is much less humane, giving a person the glimmer of hope that pain might be saved—until the wound is slowly and uncomfortably exposed for all to see.

I still remember the day our foreclosure became a reality. It hit with such a ruthless blow that there was no thought of gathering necessities, like coats from the attic or boots from the basement. No, on that dark day, all one could do was cling to cherished memories and grab a few meaningless items that just happened to be located along the dismal path to the door.

Later that winter, I longed for so many things I had taken for granted in earlier years, like my favorite coat. I knew right where it had been in the attic, but hadn't thought of it on that miserable summer day so long ago. As the days grew colder, I wandered into my favorite thrift shop, hoping to find something to take its place.

"We've got a lot of coats right here," the man at the thrift shop had said, pointing to a rack. "You look like you could use one."

I was already two steps ahead of him. There, on the rack, I saw a coat just like my own. Putting it on and plunging my hand into the pocket, I retrieved a card I had left there long ago. Taking a deep breath, I looked away so the man wouldn't see the tears welling in my eyes.

In my own coat, I was home again.

Looking at the sign above the rack, I noticed that coats were $6.00. I pulled the coat a little tighter, wanting to feel its warmth for a few more moments before hanging it back with the others. I had about $2.50 in my pocketbook, not even half enough to buy the coat.

In the days that followed, I couldn't stop thinking about my coat, saving every penny until I had the

$6.00. When I finally pulled open the door of the thrift shop, I wondered if the coat was long gone.

But there it was.

I happily paid for the coat, pulling it around me and twirling like a little girl as I headed out the door. Not only was I warmer, I had recovered a piece of my home.

Just then, I saw a woman walking straight toward me, wearing nothing but flip-flops and a dress that was thin as a slip.

"Oh, you have the coat," she said quietly. "I was hoping it would still be here. Been coming back every few days to check. Still saving my money."

Looking into her eyes, I knew what would happen next. It occurred in one fluid motion, with only two words spoken.

"Here," I said, handing her my coat.

"Thanks," she whispered.

13

Drinking It All In

The bus driver was humming a little tune and that set my mind wandering in a different direction. I thought of Grady and smiled as he entered my thoughts. I remembered the days when I had heard Grady humming at the soup kitchen and turned to greet him, only to plunge headfirst into a wall of alcohol.

Grady's Decision:

Grady was kind and gentle, but he was also one of those people who was consumed by alcohol. Sure, he drank the stuff, but it swallowed a lot more of him than he did of it. He woke up one day and found himself knee-deep in trouble and on his way to jail.

After Grady returned from a quick trip to prison, he spent more time than usual at the soup kitchen, and we had some fine talks over chicken and dumplings, his favorite. Time and again, he told me he wanted to change his ways. Then he'd walk out the door, visit the same places, do the same things—and come back to tell me how bad he felt about it. I wasn't convinced he'd ever muster up the willpower to do anything different.

Grady knew drinking was off limits at the soup kitchen, but as I said, every once in awhile I could tell he had tipped back a bottle or two before he came in.

"That ol' Teddy, don't you know, I'm gonna kick his A-S-S," Grady announced loudly one day, startling everyone in the room.

They all heard him, but the Soupers kept right on eating, eyes in the middle of their plates. The room was silent except for metal spoons clinking against china dishes.

You need to know a couple of things about my soup kitchens. I never serve food in Styrofoam bowls or on paper plates; and, my goodness, I certainly don't use plastic spoons and forks. It's about dignity. People deserve to eat with real plates and silverware, just like we do at home. This isn't a picnic, after all. It's lunch or dinner or whatever you want to call it. It's their daily nourishment, and I'm not about to serve it up like some fast food joint.

And I'm determined to preserve a little atmosphere, too. I have flowers on the tables and colored placemats that change with the seasons. That sets the tone for order in the room, and for the most part, people respect it.

Ushering Grady toward the door that day, I said, "You go on along now. People don't need to hear you talking like—"

Before I could finish, he smiled real big and looked around the room saying, "You know, Pastor Dale, sometimes I might say things I don't really mean. I'm just joshin' with you. You know why that is?"

He waited until he knew he had the room's attention.

"It's 'cause I've had a little nip."

And then he would laugh and laugh like it was the funniest thing on earth. He thought that joke about the "little nip" made everything just fine.

I responded with a look that let him know I didn't agree.

"Grady," I said after he'd had some time to sober up, "you'll never stop drinking unless you take a hard look at the characters you hang out with. Some people just pull each other down," I said, "and that's not good for anybody."

Little by little, it seemed like my words started to sneak their way into his heart. I don't know how he did it, but after a long road with a lot of sharp curves, he managed to get himself away from the people who were tearing him down.

You know, separating himself from negative people changed Grady's world. He finally stopped drinking and sometimes he even talks about helping out at the soup kitchen or going to church.

Grady taught me this much. You have to reach deep inside and make a change if you want something different out of life.

Back on the bus, I thought about how Grady reminded me of Daddy. It wasn't just his humming—or even the alcohol—he was built a lot like Daddy, too. Both were tall, dark, and thin, with glasses that seemed to give them a completely different view of life. Suddenly, I found myself remembering my home, so many years earlier.

Dancing with Daddy:

As a little girl, there was nothing I liked more than dancing and singing with my daddy. I had part of his name; he had most of my heart.

I loved it best when he twirled me around the room. Laughing in the way that only little girls with their daddies can do, I hoped it would never end. But all too soon, he would fall asleep, and I wondered why the fun always stopped so suddenly. It was as if we were playing musical chairs, but Daddy stopped and the music kept playing. Many years passed before I understood that the dancing was usually fueled by alcohol that ultimately lulled him to sleep.

Daddy's own "little nips" sparked his personality, and he loved to joke around. When he met someone on the street Daddy would say, "Can you loan me four quarters?" The answer was almost always, "Nope, I just have a dollar bill." Then he would laugh, grab the dollar, and say, "That'll do."

I'm glad I didn't know much about the drinking because I loved Daddy's humming and singing most of all. He had the gift of music, treating me to short melodies every day after school when we walked hand-in-hand to the mailbox, long before the fire.

But church was where Daddy really shined, joining in my Uncle Preston's singing group called the Sons of Joy. Those men could sing the Gospel like nobody's business, and everyone prayed that Daddy would be sober on Sundays so he could join them. Matter of fact, it was his gentle tenor voice that added the Joy to their name. At least that's how I saw it.

Unfortunately, there were too many Sundays when prayers weren't exactly answered.

Daddy and Grady had another thing in common. Both had spent some time in jail, although each was far too kind to be considered a jailbird.

I remember one day, when Ken and I had just started dating. I turned to him and said, "We're going somewhere special today."

"Where's that?" Ken had asked, probably hoping we were going out to eat.

I looked him straight in the eye and said, "We're going to the Georgetown prison to see my daddy. Money's been a big deal in our house ever since he was laid off from work, and he landed in jail . . .they called it "non-support," I think. Makes no sense to me because he's always been my biggest supporter. Guess that's why I want to be there for him. He's my daddy and it makes me feel just awful to think about him being all alone."

Wondering if this would change how Ken was feeling about me, I added quietly, "And if you don't want to go out with me anymore, that's okay."

"That don't change nothin' Dale," Ken had said. "Now let's go."

Daddy was in jail for several months, and when he got out, he lived in a trailer on our property. It was the best way Mommy and Daddy knew to keep our family together despite their differences. He might have been out of work, but he was still full of love.

Looking out the window of the bus, I dabbed my sleeve against my eyes, soaking up a few tears. Thoughts of Daddy were always bittersweet. Just then, my thoughts shifted ever so slightly.

Naomi's Challenge:

At the soup kitchen, a young mother was sitting across the table from us and it was obvious she was totally out of it—right in the middle of the day. Her eyes were like slits, and the small part of them I could see was beet red. In her lap was a crying baby, although she seemed to hardly notice.

I leaned across the table and whispered to her, "You need to come with me."

I got her downstairs where she could sit on a cot and calm the child.

"Girl, you need to take care of your little one, and you can't do that when you're like this. What's your name?" I asked.

She started right in on me, shaking her head and saying, "It's Naomi, but I don't have to listen to you, Miss Dale. You don't even know—"

Before she could finish I jumped in. "Oh I probably do know, Naomi—maybe more than you could ever imagine."

Just then, I stopped and looked away. For some reason, this young girl had opened a door I had never been quite ready to walk through. I wanted to hold on to the silence for a moment, gathering up some old thoughts I had carried around for years, like worn photographs neatly folded inside a tattered wallet.

Then, the words started to move. "Naomi, I've never shared this with anyone else before, but for some reason, I need to say it now." I paused to get my breath.

"I was nothing but a little girl when I figured out that my daddy was drinking an awful lot. And as soon as I got used to that, I came home and found my mommy in the same condition, laid out on the sofa. Scared me to death."

I went on, as Naomi listened.

"But, it's like this. My mommy was a hard worker and a great cook. She had a heart as good as gold and, oh, how she loved to take care of everyone! She was a strong, proud woman who was dressed to the nines every day, with a perfect manicure and beautiful clothes. No one would have guessed she ever took a drink."

The memories were talking on their own now.

"Oh, how I loved her. And Daddy, too. It's not really the drinking that I remember about them. It's what they taught me about working hard and loving people. Mommy said everyone deserves to be loved, and I heard that from Daddy, too. Looking back, I realize it wasn't anything they had to work at—it's just how they lived. It was how they lived! If someone needed help, they gave it; if a neighbor knocked at the door, they answered, even at two in the morning. Not like today where everyone has to call first and make an appointment just to say hello. Even though they struggled with their own *marriage, they never thought twice about helping someone else."*

Back on the bus, I reflected on that for a moment. Funny, I didn't see this clearly until I was replaying a long-ago talk with a perfect stranger in my mind.

Thoughts of that discussion awakened something deep inside me—something stirring like a big old pot of soup with the lid trembling from the churning steam inside. It was something I'd never realized before. I was destined to connect with Naomi and every other poor soul who ever crossed my path. I couldn't have turned away if I wanted to. It was in my blood.

My thoughts turned back to Naomi.

The words kept flowing; my heart took the lead. "Naomi, you've got a beautiful little girl in your lap. She's going to need you more and more as she grows up, and there will be others who need you, too. In fact, you're helping me right now, just by listening."

I looked at the child in her lap and continued. "When I was a little girl, my mommy meant the world to me—she still does. I think about her all the time."

The baby whimpered and Naomi rocked her to silence.

My eyes grew watery, but I went on with the story. "I remember standing on the stage at my first junior high school concert, anxiously searching the audience to find Mommy's face. But it wasn't there. I saw so many faces, so many mothers, but not my own. She wasn't there. Tears streamed down my cheeks that night as I sang words that fell to the ground before the melody could catch up with them. Later, I rushed home to find my mommy asleep next to the bottle that had blocked her way to the door."

"Oh my," Naomi mumbled.

I looked off into space without stopping, "You know, Naomi, at the time, it hurt so bad it made me angry. Today, I realize that she couldn't help herself. It was her way of getting back at life for forcing her to endure the deaths of four of her own children. Four babies! Do you know any other mother who lost four little ones? That wretched experience ripped her heart to pieces and I can't say that it wouldn't have done the same to me, or anyone else for that matter. Despite all the help she gave to those around her, Mommy lost four babies—two sets of twins—at just four and six months old. I'm not sure what happened," my voice grew softer, "but those were my little brothers and sisters."

I caught my breath and added, "I never knew them."

The young mother clutched her baby a little closer and murmured, "Oh no, no. I'm so sorry. But Miss Dale, look at you now. That's all behind you."

And I replied, "Yeah I'm here, Naomi, but I haven't always been here. Oh, my no! And it's been a slow road with plenty of bumps. It took me a long, long time, but I finally realized that life is a little easier with Jesus Christ right smack dab in the middle of it all. But, you know, even with that, life isn't just about prayer all day long. You still have to clean the house, do the dishes, and deal with a dirty diaper now and then. What I'm saying is, you still have to live your life. And the way you live it makes a great big old world of difference."

"But I don't know how . . ." she started in, genuinely searching for an answer.

"Naomi, here's where you come in. You've got to look deep, deep inside yourself to find the reasons behind the alcohol. Sometimes those reasons are covered under years of hurt and piles of mistakes, and it takes a long time and a whole lot of work to find them. I'm here to listen if that will help."

As Naomi considered that, Antonio shuffled down the steps of the soup kitchen, carrying a load of dirty dishes to the sink.

"How's it going Pastor Dale," he called across the room.

"Oh just fine, Antonio, just fine," I hollered back.

And with that, my thoughts turned to Antonio.

Antonio's Heart:

Antonio was one of my regular Soupers. In fact, he was the first person to walk through the door of that particular soup kitchen. He looked like any man you might see on the street, but once you got to know him, he had a smile that just pulled you in whether you wanted it to or not. And he had a good heart to go along with that great big grin.

This sudden interruption reminded me of how I had first met Antonio, when he lived in a tent in the woods behind the soup kitchen. He treated that tent like his castle, and the soup kitchen offered the food he needed to get through the day.

All that time, Antonio thought he was feeding his stomach. Turns out we fed his heart a little bit, too.

Antonio's life is so different now than the time I first met him, when he was drinking every day just to get through his own bumps in the road. Before long, he hooked up with a bad crowd that turned his precious tent castle into big mess. It was only a matter of time before the cops did away with the whole thing. I understood the reasons, but it was really too bad, because that tent was Antonio's home. He took more pride in it than some people do with their big houses and expensive cars.

For some reason, through it all, Antonio never stopped coming into the soup kitchen. That meant he still had hope—because I wasn't going to let go of him. There were times when the food and conversation weren't enough, and I'd help him out when he needed a dollar or two. I didn't always know how he spent it—and others might disagree with my decision—but that's okay.

The way I see it, the good Lord doesn't ask us to judge people—just to love them. And that's what I do. It's not always up to us to decide what someone needs. We just have to do our best to help. When people have been in a warm place all day—like with us in the soup kitchen—who knows what they need to get through the night on their own?

Usually, it's not about money at all. It's about being noticed. It's about a person finally realizing that he's not invisible after all.

Some people are never going to change, but I can't give up on them. And trying to mold them into some sort of pretty shape that doesn't fit them right isn't the answer. I can only help them walk their own walk. It might be hard for you to understand but that's just how it is. We've all sinned.

Anything I provide—food, support, money—comes with love and a prayer. I let the good Lord handle the rest. Christ didn't come to be waited on by others or to be picky about who he hung out with. He just came to serve. I'm trying my best to follow that example.

I'm glad my thoughts had taken me to Antonio. He was a hard worker who had become a good friend. The more time he spent helping out at the soup kitchen, the less room he had in his life for drinking or fooling around.

Today, Antonio is a dedicated volunteer who has found a real home with a local family who took him in. Thank goodness he doesn't drink much at all any more—only when something bad happens, like a girlfriend breaking up with him. That seems to shake his world.

Other than that, he's completely turned his life around.

14

Revving the Engine

After a quick rest stop, the bus driver was starting the engine in preparation for the final few miles. It took him a couple tries to get it going. I sighed, thinking how often I had heard that familiar sound.

Ruth's Rescue:

Ruth was sitting in her car, staring straight ahead. She had tried several times to start the engine but it was not cooperating. Ruth had just finished a long and tiring day of cleaning the church next to the soup kitchen. Her age was catching up to her; she was tired and ready to go home.

But now she didn't know what to do.

Although she had been cleaning the church for years, Ruth didn't really know anyone at the soup kitchen. In fact, I think she was a little afraid of most people there, except me. Ruth and I had talked a few times. She was quiet and kind, with a strong work ethic. Now that her car wouldn't start, it pained her to think of having to ask someone for help.

There was no need for that.

When the Soupers heard the car sputter and stall, they went straight to work. A few of them were mechanics, and it wasn't long before they had her car purring like a tabby cat snuggled in a sunbeam.

Despite her fear, Ruth was too polite to leave without thanking them. It was the first time I ever saw her talk with the Soupers, but it wouldn't be the last.

A single moment can open a whole world of possibility.

Thoughts of Ruth's car had reminded me of all the vehicles we'd driven through the years. Each one had its own troubles and snags. In fact, in our 41 years of marriage, Ken and I never had a brand new car. When the family ride would break down for good, Ken was usually able to buy a hand-me-down from one of his customers. By the time we got behind the wheel, the new-car smell was miles away.

That's how Ken came across the old green truck he used to have. When it was running okay, Ken and the boys would use it to haul their lawn mowing equipment. My, how the boys hated that old thing—it embarrassed them so.

I remember one time, after they'd been mowing lawns all day, Ken took the boys to the Dairy Queen in Lewes for a cold treat. The three older boys were 10, 15, and 18, I think—the perfect age to worry about their friends' opinions of everything. When it was time to head for home, of course the old truck wouldn't start without some coaxing. That meant Troy, KJ, and Dale had to line up along the tailgate and give it a push while Ken steered.

The old truck rolled along, and the engine caught on just as Troy said, "Hurry up, let's get outta here, before anybody sees us!"

There were other times when even a little push wouldn't work and Ken would take the screwdriver and touch two parts on the starter to jolt it to life. As soon as it took off, we'd all jump inside and away we'd go. That screwdriver was as important to us as the keys—maybe even more so.

And then there was the noise. My, how that truck would backfire! I always knew when Ken was coming home from work because I could hear the ruckus a mile away. Soon as I heard it, I'd plunk the ice in our water glasses and everyone knew it was time for dinner.

Ken learned an important lesson from that old truck. It was never a good idea to start an argument just before driving away. One day, we were bickering over who-knows-what just before he left for work. As soon as he got to the highway, he was pulled over and ticketed for some minor infraction that was most likely the truck's fault. Next thing I knew, Ken was back home with his tail between his legs, making up to me.

Later, we had the old '66 Chevy. It was a two-door, held together with nothing but hardworking rust and well-timed prayer. With stubborn front windows that refused to go down, summertime rides were almost unbearable. The air conditioner was nothing more than a decorative dial on the dash, connected to a worn out system that had given up long before. We might have suffocated if it weren't for kindhearted back windows that worked like a charm. They invited in plenty of air—which was usually smoke-filled and black, straight from the exhaust. We learned to live with it, unlike people on the street who held their breath until we drove past.

Every now and then, the old Chevy needed a jump-start, too, but it usually got us where we needed to go. One of our most important trips involved going to see Troy graduate from the University of Delaware. We couldn't have been prouder, spending weeks getting the car ready for the trip up north.

A Lesson in Love:

Finally, the big day arrived. We soon learned that, not only would we see our first son graduate from college, we would also be meeting his girlfriend's parents. Troy and his girlfriend were very close, and we knew it was only a matter of time before they would get married. She was precious to us and nothing was more important than making a good impression on her family from Long Island.

Back then, a rusty '66 Chevy was not the best way to make a good impression, but we had no other way to get to Newark. So Ken and I came up with an idea. At the graduation, we would park the car as far away as possible, where no one would see us arrive or leave.

It was the perfect plan.

We beamed as we watched the kids graduate, and our smiles increased when we met the Long Island visitors. We could see where Troy's girlfriend had acquired her delightful personality; her parents couldn't have been nicer.

The evening was ideal—maybe even magical—until the girl's father spoke up.

"Dale and Ken, we want you to join us for dinner in Glasgow. Let's have some fun and celebrate with the kids."

There was an uneasy silence as their invitation floated in mid-air. I nervously glanced at Ken, saw his gears turning, and was sure he must have noticed the same in me. Smiles hid our unspoken conversation from all the others.

The curve ball had thrown off our game, but it wouldn't stop us. We knew we could keep the car out of eyeshot by parking on a side street in Glasgow. Then we'd walk down another street and land in the restaurant just in time to meet up with the others. When dinner was over, we'd exclaim that we needed to leave early—or make an excuse to stay later than the others—to avoid walking to our cars together.

Yes, our car-cover-up could still work out just fine.

With these new plans swirling through our minds, Ken and I waved to the others and began walking to the car. We paced up and down the lot, passing all the other graduates and parents, until we found our Chevy alone, huddled near the back. It was waiting right where we'd left it, like a loyal family mutt.

We hopped in, laughing as we shared our matching ideas. For once, we had outsmarted the car that couldn't be trusted.

Or so we thought.

Of course it wouldn't start. Temperamental as it was, why would we have expected it to cooperate on such an important night?

Just when we were ready to start walking, a car came into view and I breathed a sigh of relief, hoping it would be someone who could give us a jumpstart. And that's exactly what happened. With a little help, we were quickly on our way, thanks to Troy, his girlfriend, and her parents—in their brand new Mercedes!

Despite our worries, these new friends were as nice as could be. They didn't care about our car at all; they genuinely liked us, and they liked Troy too.

Over time, we visited their home in Long Island and they came to see us in Lewes. Although they had the best of everything, we could see that they had earned it through hard work. And they never looked down on us. In fact, they were so taken with our humble little home that they said it sometimes felt more comfortable than their own grand estate. When they learned that most of our things had come from yard sales and thrift stores, they were ready to go bargain shopping with me right then and there.

I'll never forget that. People who could have judged us—by the color of our skin or the condition of our car—didn't do that at all.

They just loved us.

15

The Awakening

"Dale, how're you doing?" Ken asked, tapping my shoulder. "It won't be long now, and you wanna be ready."

I stretched my neck and stopped to look from side to side. With so many people still wandering around in my head, it took a while to get my bearings. I felt a sort of sadness and separation, not ready to let any of those precious people go.

I looked around some more. There I was, on a bus. Not just any old bus—it was the famous one that had appeared many times on TV. This was a life-changing vehicle, capable of driving people right into an amazing, uncharted future. We were rolling down the road in that bus, getting closer and closer to our new home, a yet-to-be-seen place that had sprung to life in just one week.

But I knew it wasn't that easy; our home didn't really spring to life at all. A lot of people had worked around the clock to make it happen. They must have stayed up late, gotten up early, stubbed their toes, and pinched their fingers. Normally, that's where *I* would have been: among the people toiling night and day to help someone else.

I shifted in my seat, feeling incredibly uncomfortable, wishing the bus would slow down so I could jump off and run, as far away as I could. But the wheels kept turning; farmhouses and mailboxes were flying by. In fact, it seemed like we were gaining speed with every minute.

I was helpless to change that.

The past few days were fresh on my mind. Despite the fact that I had cherished the time with Ken and Brooks, a sense of loneliness had been ripping at my heart. The feeling seemed to grow stronger with every mile we traveled.

Something had been missing.

That's when the daydreams had started. They had lifted me up and carried me to places beyond imagination, stirring a flame that kept me warm and content.

I shook my head, continuing to return from my thoughts. Looking around, I knew the people were miles and miles behind me. No matter how hard I tried, I couldn't get them back. Even if I had the time to remember each one, I couldn't be sure it would ever be the same. I couldn't force the memories to return.

I couldn't bring the precious people back.

Searching for a sense of comfort, I whispered the verse that had always made me smile, "If you love me, take care of my sheep." I followed the image, and it quietly led me to the parable of the sheep in Luke.

> *"Suppose one of you has a hundred sheep and loses one of them. Doesn't he leave the ninety-nine in the open country and go after the lost sheep until he finds it? And when he finds it, he joyfully puts it on his shoulders and goes home. Then he calls his friends and neighbors together and says, 'Rejoice with me; I have found my lost sheep.'"*

At that moment, things I had always known but never seen became incredibly clear.

Each one of us has the capacity for life-changing compassion. But it's so much more than that. Every changed life—every sheep that is found—has the magnitude to transform other lives, including her own.

It happens very slowly, one at a time, and every sheep matters. Even the ones that are dirty or scared or sick or hungry. Every single sheep counts. Each one is precious.

Right then I knew that I didn't need daydreams or imagination to get the people back. They would never leave. In fact, they had been there for years, like a steadfast flock, even when I didn't realize it. They were with me each day when I woke before dawn to mix up the soup. They boldly helped me find gentle words when I encountered a woman lying in a cemetery, devastated over losing her entire family in a car accident. They guided my hand when I bravely plunged it into a boardwalk trashcan to stop a starving stranger from eating leftover food that had just been soaked in spit. Now invisible, each one of these people—once lost sheep of their own—had been by my side as I steered someone over a bump in the road.

I looked around the bus and smiled, feeling the sudden sense of warmth and camaraderie.

Every single empty seat was filled with sheep.

And we were joyfully headed home.

EPILOGUE

My heart overflows with joy and gratitude. When I stepped off the bus, I arrived at a place that is so much more than home.

It is my eighteenth soup kitchen.

Matthew 6: 31-33

"So do not worry, saying, 'What shall we eat?' or 'What shall we drink?' or 'What shall we wear?' Your heavenly Father knows that you need them. But seek first his kingdom and his righteousness, and all these things will be given to you as well."

ABOUT MICHAEL SYMON

Michael Symon cooks with soul. Growing up in a Greek and Sicilian family, the Cleveland native creates boldly-flavored, deeply satisfying dishes at his four restaurants in America's heartland: Lola, Lolita, Roast and B Spot. He also shares his exuberant, approachable cooking style and infectious laugh with viewers as an Iron Chef on the Food Network and as co-host of ABC's *The Chew*.

In 2009, Michael earned The James Beard Foundation Award for Best Chef Great Lakes and in 2000 *Gourmet* magazine chose Lola as one of *America's Best Restaurants*.

In 2010, Michael appeared on four Food Network/ Cooking Channel shows, hosting *Food Feuds* and *Cook Like an Iron Chef*, judging season three of *The Next Iron Chef* and competing on *Iron Chef America*.

Michael published his first cookbook, *Michael Symon's Live to Cook – Recipes and Techniques to Rock Your Kitchen*, in 2009, sharing home cook-friendly recipes that draw on the flavors of his heritage.

When he's not working, Michael is riding his motorcycle through Cleveland, cooking at home, playing golf, thinking about his next tattoo, gardening in the backyard and spending time with his wife, Liz, and their bullmastiff, Ruby, and Old English bulldog, Ozzy.

ABOUT THE AUTHOR

Debby Coughlan met Dale Dunning when she volunteered at the soup kitchen and assisted with the family's nomination for *Extreme Makeover: Home Edition*. Their friendship developed when the two decided to collaborate on a book about Dale's life.

The author specializes in helping people share their inspiring stories. Her first book, "In the Middle of the Line," recounts a young orphan's extraordinary journey from war-torn Liberia to his new home with an American family.

Debby lives with her husband, Dean, in Pasadena, Maryland. She spends most of her time writing, traveling, and enjoying time with family.